Look at the letters and say the sounds.

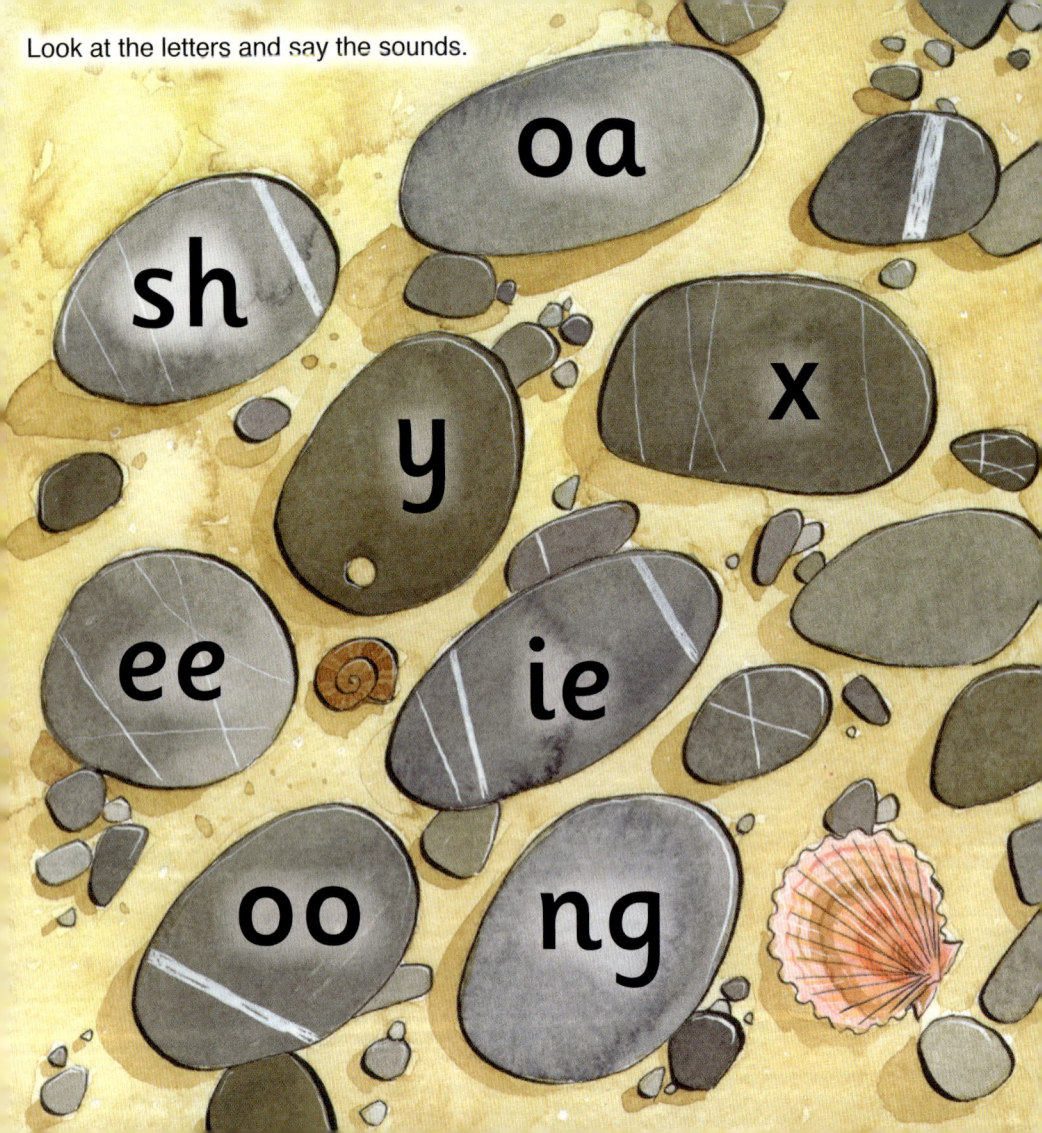

Say the word *sun* and listen out for the sounds: *sun* – /s-u-n/.
(There is one sound dot underneath the sun for each sound in the word.)

Say the word *fish* and listen out for the sounds: *fish* – /f-i-sh/.

Say the word *crab* and listen out for the sounds: *crab* – /c-r-a-b/.